One day Pete went to the island.
'I will find the treasure,' he said.

On the map was a big rock.
On the island was a big rock.

'Can you see the treasure?'
said Beaky.
'No!' said Pete.
'The treasure is not here.'

On the map was a tree.
On the island was a tree.

'Can you see the treasure?'
said Beaky.
'No!' said Pete.
'The treasure is not here.'

On the map was a cave.
On the island was a cave.

'Can you see the treasure?'
said Beaky.
'Yes!' said Pete.
'It is in the hole.'

Pete got into the hole.
'I will get the treasure,' he said.

'I can see a dragon,' said Beaky.
'What dragon?' said Pete.

'Thundering Cannonballs!'
said Pete.